the CAT
& the
COFFEE
DRINKERS

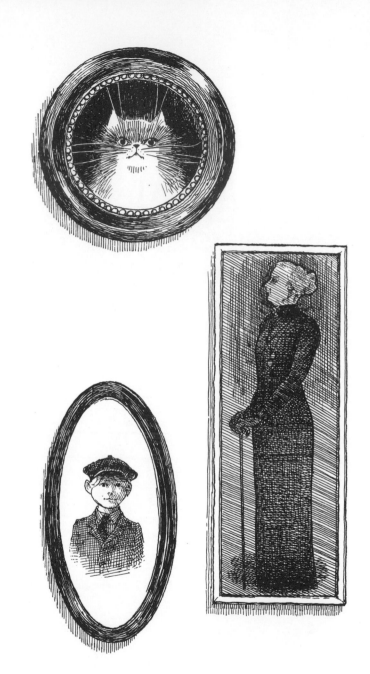

the CAT
& the
COFFEE
DRINKERS

by
MAX STEELE

with drawings by **ERIK BLEGVAD**

Harper & Row, Publishers • New York, Evanston, and London

The original version of "The Cat and the Coffee Drinkers"
appeared in *The New Yorker*, May 11, 1963.

for Oliver Whittinghill Steele

Only the five-year-old children who were sent to the kindergarten of Miss Effie Barr had any idea what they were learning in that one-room schoolhouse, and they seldom told anyone, and certainly not grown people.

My father was sent to her when he was five years old, and thirty years later when no one had much money, I was sent to her. Even though ours was no longer a small Southern town, and even though she was already in her seventies the first time I saw her, Miss Effie had known all the children in her school a year, and often longer, before they appeared before her for lessons. My mother, with proper gloves and hat, began taking me to call on her when I was four.

1

It was a good place to visit. The house was a large gray one with elegant white columns, and it was set well back from the same street we lived on. Until the Depression the Barrs had owned the entire block and theirs was the only house on it.

There were mossy brick steps leading up from the hitching post to the gravel walk which curved between overgrown boxwoods to the low porch with its twelve slender columns. There in the summer in the shade of the water oaks Miss Effie, dressed in black, would be sitting, knitting or embroidering while her big gray cat sat at, and sometimes on, her feet. Slow uncertain music would be coming through the open windows from the music room, where her older sister, Miss Hattie, gave piano lessons.

Miss Effie never seemed to watch a child on such visits, or offer him anything like cookies or lemonade, or say anything to endear herself to a youngster. Instead she would talk lady-talk with the mother and, hardly pausing, say to the waiting child, "You can pull up the wild onions on the lawn if you've nothing better to do." There was no suggestion in her voice that it was a game or that there would be a reward. She simply stated what could be done if one took a notion. Usually a child did.

There was no nonsense about Miss Effie. One morning in late September my mother and I were standing with eleven other mothers and children on the wide porch. Miss Effie looked everyone over carefully from where she stood with one hand on the screen door. She checked a

3

list in the other hand against the faces on the porch to be sure that these were the children she had chosen from the forty or more who had visited her in the summer.

Apparently satisfied, or at least reconciled to another year of supplementing her income (for no Southern lady of her generation "worked"), she opened the door wide and said in her indifferent tone, "Children inside." When one mother tried to lead her reluctant son into the dark parlor, Miss Effie said, "Mothers outside." She pushed the big cat out with her foot and said, "You too, Mr. Thomas."

When the children were all inside and the mothers outside, Miss Effie latched the screen, thanked the mothers for bringing the children, and reminded them that classes began at eight thirty and ended

4

at noon. The tuition of two dollars a week
would be acceptable each Friday, and
each child as part of his training should
be given the responsibility for delivering
the money in an envelope bearing the
parent's signature. She thanked them
again in such a way that there was nothing for them to do except wander together
in a group down the gravel walk.

Miss Effie then turned to us, standing somewhat closer together than was necessary in the center of the dark parlor, and said, "Since this is your first day, I want to show you everything. Then you won't be wondering about things while you should be listening."

She made us look at the Oriental carpet, the grandfather clock, the bookcases of leather-bound volumes, and the shelves on which were collections of rocks, shells, birds' nests, and petrified wood. She offered to let us touch, just this once, any of these things.

She would not let us into the music room, but she indicated through the door the imported grand piano, the red plush seat where Miss Hattie sat during lessons, the music racks, the ferns, and the window seats, which she said were full of

6

sheet music. "You're never to go in there," she said. "I don't go in there myself."

Next, she showed us the dining room, the den, and the hallway, and then at the foot of the stairs she said, "We're going upstairs, and then you'll never go up there again." Barbara Ware, one of the three girls, began to whimper. "Don't worry," Miss Effie said. "You'll come

back down. But there'll be no reason to go up again. I want you to see everything so you won't have to ask personal questions, which would certainly be the height of impoliteness, wouldn't it? I mean, if you started wanting to know, without my telling you, where I sleep and which window is Miss Hattie's, I'd think you were rude, wouldn't I? I'll show you everything so you won't be tempted to ask personal questions."

We went up the stairs, and she showed us her room and where she kept her shoes (in the steps leading up to the side of the four-poster bed), where she hung her clothes (in two large wardrobes), and where she kept her hatbox (in a teakwood sea chest). The cat, she said, slept on the sea chest if he happened to be home at night.

She then knocked on the door of Miss Hattie's room and asked her sister if we might look in. Miss Hattie agreed to a short visit. After that Miss Effie showed us the upstairs bathroom and that the bathtub faucet dripped all night and that was why the towel was kept under it.

Downstairs again, she let us see the new kitchen, which was built in 1900, and the back porch, which had been screened in only four years before, with a small door through which the cat could come and go as he liked. We were as fascinated by everything as we would have been if we had never seen a house before.

"Now, out the back door. All of you." She made us all stand on the ground, off the steps, while she lowered herself step by step with the aid of a cane which she kept on a nail by the door. "Now you've seen my house, and you won't see it again. Unless I give your mothers fruitcake and coffee at Christmas. And I don't think I will. Not this year. Do you ever get tired of fruitcake and coffee at Christmas?"

We said we did since it was clear that she did.

"Over there is the barn, and we'll see it some other time. And that is the greenhouse, and we'll be seeing it often. And here is the classroom where we'll be." She pointed with her cane to a square brick building, which before the Civil War had been the kitchen. The door was open.

She shepherded us along the brick walk with her cane, not allowing any of us near enough to her to topple her over. At the open door she said, "Go on in."

We crowded in, and when we were all through the door, she summoned us back out. "Now which of you are boys?" The nine boys raised their hands, following her lead. "And which girls?" The three girls had already separated themselves from the boys and nodded together. "All right then, young gentlemen," she said, regarding us, "let's let the young ladies enter first, or I may think you're all young ladies."

The girls, looking timid and pleased, entered. We started in after them.

"Wait just a minute, young gentlemen," she said. "Haven't you forgotten something?" We looked about for another girl.

"Me!" she announced. "You've forgotten me!" She passed through our huddle, separating us with her stick, and

11

marched into the brick kitchen.

Inside and out, the kitchen was mainly of brick. The walls and floor were brick, and the huge chimney and hearth, except for a closet-cupboard on each side of it, were brick. The ceiling, however, was of beams and broad boards, and the windows were of wavy glass in casements that opened out like shutters. There were three large wooden tables and at each table four chairs.

Again she had to show us everything. The fireplace would be used only in the coldest weather, she said. At other times an iron stove at one side of the room would be used. A captain's chair between the fireplace and the stove was her own and not to be touched by us. A sewing table, overflowing with yarn and knitting needles, was for her own use and not for ours. One cupboard, the one near her, held dishes. She opened its door. She would let us see in the other cupboard later. The tables and chairs and, at the far end of the room, the pegs for coats were all ours to do with as we pleased. It was, she explained, our schoolroom, and therefore, since we were young ladies and

13

gentlemen, she was sure we would keep it clean.

As a matter of fact, she saw no reason why we should not begin with the first lesson: Sweeping and Dusting. She opened the other cupboard and showed us a mop, bucket, rags, brushes, and three brooms. We were not divided into teams; we were not given certain areas to see who could sweep his area cleanest. We were simply told that young ladies should naturally be able to sweep and that young gentlemen at some times in their lives would certainly be expected to sweep a room clean.

The instruction was simple: "You get a good grip on the handle and set to." She handed out the three brooms and started the first three boys sweeping from the fireplace toward the front door. She made simple corrections: "You'll raise a dust, flirting the broom upward. Keep it near the floor. Hold lower on the handle. You'll get more dirt. Don't bend over. You'll be tired before the floor is clean."

Miss Effie corrected the series of sweepers from time to time while she made a big red enamel coffeepot of coffee on a small alcohol stove. Each child was given a turn with the broom before the job was finished. Since the room had not been swept, she admitted, all summer, there was a respectable pile of brick dust, sand, and sweepings near the door by the time she said, "We'll have lunch now." It was already ten o'clock. "After lunch I'll teach you how to take up trash and to dust. Everyone needs to know that."

"Lunch," it happened, was half a mug of coffee each. One spoon of sugar, she

15

said, was sufficient, if we felt it necessary
to use sugar at all (she didn't), and there
was milk for those who could not or
would not (she spoke as though using
milk were a defect of character) take
their coffee black. I daresay not any of
us had ever had coffee before, and Robert
Barnes said he hadn't.

"Good!" Miss Effie said. "So you have
learned something today."

Miriam Wells, however, said that her parents wouldn't approve of her drinking coffee.

"Very well," Miss Effie said. "Don't drink it. And the next time I offer you any, if I ever do, simply say 'No, thank you, ma'am.'" (The next day Miriam Wells was drinking it along with the rest of us.) "Let's get this clear right this minute—your parents don't need to know what you do when you're under my instruction."

Her firm words gave us a warm feeling, and from that moment on, the schoolroom became a special, safe, and rather secret place.

That day we learned, further, how to rinse out mugs and place them in a pan to be boiled later, how to take up trash, and how to dust. At noon we were taught how to put on our sweaters or coats and how to hold our caps in our left hands until we were outside. We also learned how to approach, one at a time, our teacher (or any lady we should happen to be visiting) and say thank you (for the coffee or whatever we had been served) and how to say good-bye and turn and leave the room without running or laughing.

The next morning Robert Barnes was waiting on his steps when I walked by his house. Since he and I lived nearer to the Barrs than any of the other children, we were the first to arrive. We walked up the grassy drive as we had been told to do and along the brick walk and into the schoolhouse.

Miss Effie sat in her captain's chair brushing the large gray cat which lay on a tall stool in front of her. We entered without speaking. Without looking up, Miss Effie said, "Now, young gentlemen, let's try that again—outside. Take off your caps before you step through the door and say 'Good morning, ma'am' as you come through the door. Smile if you feel like it. Don't if you don't." She herself did not smile as we went out and came back in the manner she had suggested. However, this time she looked directly at us when she returned our "good mornings." Each child who entered in what she felt to be a rude way was sent out to try again.

Strangely enough she did not smile at anyone. She treated each child as an adult and each lesson as though it were a serious task. Even though there were occasional crying scenes or temper tantrums

19

among us, she herself never lost her firm, rational approach. Sitting in her captain's chair, dressed in black from neck to toe except for a cameo, small gold loop earrings, and a gold and opal ring on her right hand, she was usually as solemn and considerate as a judge on his bench.

The third day she was again brushing the cat as we entered. She waited until we were all properly in before addressing us as a class. "This is Mr. Thomas. He's a no-good cat, and he doesn't like children, so leave him alone. I'd have nothing to do with him myself except that he happens to belong to me because his mother and grandmother belonged to me. They were no-good either. But since he does belong to me and since he is here, we may as well talk about cats."

She showed us how to brush a cat, the

spots under his neck where he liked to
be rubbed, how he didn't like his ears or
whiskers touched, how his ears turned to
pick up sounds, how he stretched and

shut his paw pads when he was tickled on
the stomach or feet, and how he twitched
his tail when annoyed. "Mr. Thomas is a
fighter," she said—and she let us look at
the scars from a dozen or more serious

fights—"and he's getting too old to fight, but he hasn't got sense enough to know that."

She looked at us where we stood more or less in a large circle around her. "Now, let's see, I don't know your names. I know your mothers, but not your names." She would, she said, point to us one at a time and we were to give our names in clear, loud voices while looking her right in the eye. Then we were to choose a chair at one of the three tables.

"I hate the way most people become shy when they say their names. Be proud of it and speak up."

When the young ladies had finished giving their names, she said that they did admirably well; they chose to sit at the same table. One or two boys shouted their names in a silly fashion and had to repeat. One or two others looked away, to decide on a chair or to watch the cat, they claimed, and so had to repeat. I did not speak loud enough and had to say my name three times. One lad refused to say his name a second time, and that day and the next she called him Mr. No-Name. On Friday he did not appear, or Monday or Tuesday, and the next week a new boy from the waiting list gave his name in a perfect fashion and took Mr. No-Name's place.

We learned about cats and names the third day then. The following day Barbara Ware and Robert Barnes distinguished themselves by claiming to like their coffee black with no sugar, just the way Miss Effie was convinced it should be drunk.

At the end of the second week we reviewed what we had learned by sweeping and dusting the room again. And each day we practiced coming in and leaving properly and saying our names in a way that sounded as though we were proud of them and of ourselves—which by then we were.

The third week, putting down the cat brush and shooing Mr. Thomas off the stool, Miss Effie said that she too was proud of the way we identified ourselves with eyes level and unblinking. "But now," she said, "I want to teach you to give a name that is not your own—without any shiftiness."

She sat with both thin hands clasping the arms of her chair and gave a short lecture. Not everyone, she said, was entitled to know your name. Some people of a certain sort would ask when it was none of their business. It would be unnecessarily rude to tell them so. But we could simply tell such people a name that had nothing whatever to do with our own. She did not mention kidnappings, but talked rather about ruthless salesmen, strangers on buses and trains, and tramps and beggars wandering through the neighborhood.

For the purpose of practice, all of the young ladies would learn to give in a courteous, convincing manner the rather dated, unconvincing name "Polly Livingstone." The boys would be, when asked, "William Johnson" (a name I can still give with much more conviction than my own). That day and the next we each gave our own names before the coffee break, and after coffee, our false names. We liked the exercises in which we went up to her, shook her hand if she offered it, and gave our false names, confronting, without staring, her solemn gaze with ours. If we smiled or twisted, we had to stand by the fireplace until we could exercise more poise.

At the end of the first month Miss Effie said that she was fairly well pleased with our progress. "I have taught you, thus far, mainly about rooms. Most people

spend most of their lives in rooms, and now you know about them."

She mentioned some of the things we had learned, like how to enter rooms: ladies first, young men bareheaded with their caps in their left hands, ready to offer their right hands to any extended, how to look a person directly in the eye and give one's name (real or false, depending on the occasion) without squirming, how to sweep and dust a room, and finally how to leave a room promptly, without lingering, but without running or giggling.

"What else have we learned about rooms?" she then asked, letting Mr. Thomas out the window onto the sunny ledge where he liked to sit.

"How to drink coffee," Miriam Wells said rather proudly.

"No," Miss Effie said, "that has to do with another series which includes how to accept things and how to get rid of things you don't want: fat meat, bones, seeds, pits, peelings, and"—she added under her breath—"parents." She paused for a moment and looked pleased, as though she might wink or smile, but her angular face did not change its expression very much. "No. Besides, I'm not pleased with the way you're drinking coffee." She then said for the first time a speech which she repeated so often that by the end of the year we sometimes shouted it in our play on the way home. "Coffee is a beverage to be enjoyed for its flavor. It is not a food to be enriched with milk and sugar. Only certain types of people try to gain nourishment from it. In general they are the ones, I suspect, who show their emotions in public." (We had, I'm sure, no idea what the speech meant.) She expected us by June—possibly by Christmas —to be drinking it black.

"Is there anything else we need to know about rooms?" she asked.

"How to build them," Phillip Pike said.

"That," Miss Effie said, "you can't learn from me. Unfortunately. I wish I knew."

She looked thoughtfully out the window to the ledge on which Mr. Thomas was grooming himself. "Windows!" she said. "How to clean windows."

Again the cupboard was opened, and by noon the next day we knew how to clean windows inside and out and how to adjust all the shades in a room to the same level.

When it turned cold in November—

cold enough for the stove but not the fireplace, we settled down to the real work which had given Miss Effie's kindergarten its reputation: Reading. Miss Effie liked to read, and it was well-known in the town and especially among the public-school teachers that the two or three hundred children she had taught had grown up reading everything they could find. She assured us that even though we were only five years old we would be reading better than the third-grade schoolchildren by the end of the year.

Each morning the stove was already hot when we arrived. She would brush Mr. Thomas awhile; then when we were all in our places and warm, she would hand out our reading books, which we opened every day to the first page and laid flat before us on the tables. While we

looked at the first page she began heating
the big red enamel pot of coffee, and also,
because we needed nourishment to keep
warm, a black iron pot of oatmeal. Then
Miss Effie would sit down, allow Mr.
Thomas to jump into her lap, and begin
reading—always from the first page in
an excited tone. She would read to the
point exactly where we had finished the
day before, so that from necessity she

32

read faster each day while we turned our pages, which we knew by heart, when we saw her ready to turn hers.

Then one after another we went up to her and sat on Mr. Thomas's stool by the stove and read aloud to her while those at the tables either listened, or read, or played with architectural blocks. The child on the stool was rewarded at the end of each sentence with two spoonfuls of oatmeal if he read well, one if not so well. Since we each read twice, once before coffee and once after, we did not really get hungry before we left the school at noon. Of course those who read fast and well ate more oatmeal than the others.

In addition to the reading lessons, which were the most important part of the day, we learned to take money and shopping lists to Mr. Zenacher's grocery store, to pay for groceries, and to bring them back with the change. Usually two or three of us went together to the store on the next block. At the same time three or four others might be learning to paint flowerpots or to catch frying-size chickens in the chicken yard back of the barn.

On sunny days that winter we would all go out to the greenhouse for an hour and learn to reset ferns and to start bulbs on wet beds of rock. In March we learned how to rake Miss Effie's tennis court, to fill in the holes with powdery sand, and to tie strings properly so that later a yardman could mark the lines with lime. The tennis court was for rent in the afternoons to high school girls and boys during the spring and summer.

By Eastertime we were all proficient sweepers, dusters, shoppers, bulb-setters,

readers, and black-coffee drinkers. Miss
Effie herself, now that spring was almost
in the air, hated to sit all morning by the
stove where we'd been all winter. Usually
after an hour or so of reading all aloud
and at once, we would follow her into
the yards and prune the first-breath-of-
spring, the jessamines, the yellow bells,
and the peach and pear trees. We kept
the branches we cut off, and we stuck

them in buckets of water in the green-house. Miss Effie printed a sign which said "Flowers for Sale," and we helped her tie it to a tree near the sidewalk. In addition to the flowering branches which we had forced, she sold ferns and the jonquils that we had set, which were now in bud.

All in all, spring was a busy time. And I remember only one other thing we learned. One warm May morning we arrived to find Mr. Thomas, badly torn about the ears, his eyes shut, his breathing noisy, on a folded rug near the open door of the schoolhouse. We wanted to pet him and talk to him, but Miss Effie, regarding him constantly, said No, that he had obviously been not only a bad cat but a foolish one. She believed he had been hit by a car while running from some dogs

36

and that that was how the dogs got to him. (She and Miss Hattie had heard the fight during the night.) At any rate, he had managed to crawl under the steps where the dogs couldn't get to him anymore. At dawn she had come down and thrown hot water on the dogs and rescued him.

As soon as a boy from her cousin's office arrived (her cousin was a doctor)

she was going to teach us how to put a cat to sleep, she said.

We pointed out that he already seemed to be asleep.

"But," she explained, not taking her eyes from the cat, "we are going to put him to sleep so that he won't wake up."

"You're going to kill him?" Robert Barnes said.

"You could say that."

We were all greatly disturbed when we understood that this was the last we would see of Mr. Thomas. But Miss Effie had no sympathy, apparently, for the cat or for us. "He is suffering, and even if he is a no-good cat, he shouldn't suffer."

When Barbara Ware began to whimper, Miss Effie said, "Animals are not people." Her tone was severe enough to stop Barbara from crying.

After the boy had arrived with the package and left, Miss Effie stopped her reading, went to the cupboard, and got out a canvas bag with a drawstring top. "Now if you young ladies will follow us, I'll ask the young gentlemen to bring Mr. Thomas."

We all rushed to be the ones to lift the piece of carpet and bear Mr. Thomas after her through the garden to the toolshed. "Just wrap the carpet around him. Tight. Head and all," she instructed when we reached the toolshed. After we had him wrapped securely, Miss Effie opened the package and read the label—"Chloroform." She explained to us the properties of the chemical while we rolled the cat tighter and stuck him, tail first, into the canvas bag. Miss Effie asked us to stand back and hold our breaths. She then

39

soaked a large rag with the liquid and poured the rest directly onto the cat's head and on the carpet. She poked the rag into the rolled carpet so that it hid Mr. Thomas completely. She then drew the drawstring tight and placed the cat, bag and all, in the toolshed. She shut the door firmly and latched it. "That'll cut out the air," she said.

Back in the schoolhouse, we tried to listen as she read, without the usual excited tone, but we were all thinking about Mr. Thomas in the toolshed. "Well," she finally said, "if you will excuse me a moment, I'll go see if my cat is dead."

We watched from the windows as she walked with her cane through the garden to the toolshed. We could see her open the door and bend over the sack for a long time. At last she straightened up and

locked the door again. She came back with the same unhalting gait and stood for a moment in the sun before the open door of the schoolhouse.

"When I dismiss you, you're to go straight down the drive and straight home. And if they want to know why you're home early"—she stopped and studied the ground as though she had lost there her cameo or her words—"tell them the only thing Miss Effie had to teach you today was how to kill a cat."

Without waiting for us to leave, she walked in her usual dignified fashion down the brick walk and up the back steps and into her house, shutting the kitchen door firmly behind her. I know that that was not the last day of school, for I remember helping to spread tablecloths over the reading tables, and I remember helping to serve tea cakes to the mothers who came the last day and stood on the tennis court near the table where Miss Hattie was serving coffee. But the final, definite picture I have of Miss Effie is that of her coming through the garden from the toolshed and standing in the doorway a moment to say that she had nothing more to teach us.